TOLKIEN'S
WORLD

A COLOURING BOOK

CASSELL
ILLUSTRATED

An Hachette UK Company
www.hachette.co.uk

First published in 2015 by Cassell Illustrated,
a division of Octopus Publishing Group Ltd
Carmelite House
50 Victoria Embankment
London, EC4Y 0DZ

www.octopusbooks.co.uk

Reprinted in 2015

Copyright © Octopus Publishing Group Ltd 2015

ISBN: 978-0-75373-020-1

A CIP catalogue record for this book is available from the British Library

Printed and bound in Italy

10 9 8 7 6 5 4 3

Publisher: Samantha Warrington
Creative Director: Miranda Snow
Senior Production Manager: Katherine Hockley
Text: Anna Bowles
Editor: Phoebe Morgan

Illustration Credits:

Victor Ambrus: 12, 14-15, 30, 31

John Davis: 62, 78

Mauro Mazzara: 6, 7, 13, 18, 19, 22, 23, 24, 25, 32, 33, 34, 35, 38, 39, 42, 43, 48, 49, 50, 51, 54, 55, 58, 60, 61, 63, 68, 69, 70, 71, 72, 73, 74, 75, 76, 77, 79, 80, 82, 83, 84, 85, 86, 87, 88, 89, 90, 91, 92, 93, 94, 95,96

Ian Miller: 44, 45, 75, 81

Andrea Piparo: 4-5, 8-9,10-11, 16-17, 20-21, 26-27, 28-29, 36-37, 40-41, 46-47,

WELCOME TO ARDA...

Have you ever wanted to travel through Middle-earth with Thorin and Company or the Fellowship of the Ring? Or visit the Undying Lands in the uttermost West and look upon the Trees of the Valar?

The gorgeous line art you'll find in these pages sets the scene for you to add colour and detail to beloved characters and places as you've seen them in your mind a hundred times, reading *The Hobbit, The Silmarillion,* and *The Lord of the Rings.*

Bring Tolkien's world to life the way you've always imagined it, join the Fellowship of the Ring as they journey through perilous lands, or take up arms in the Battle of the Pelennor.

Turn the page and surround yourself with the magic of Middle-earth.

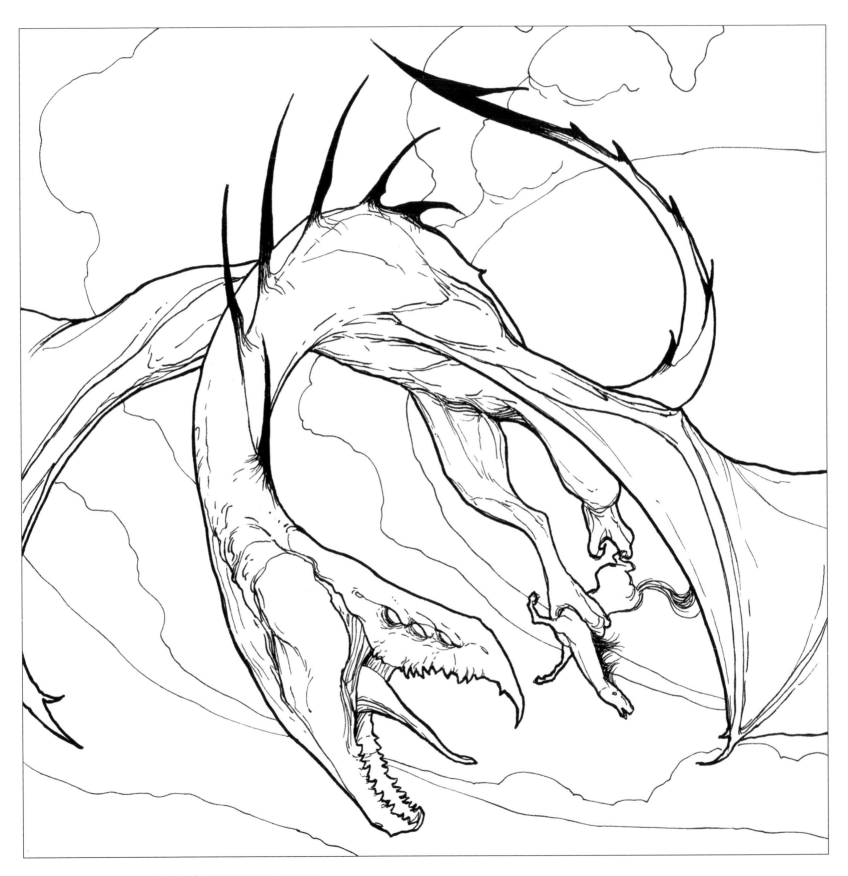

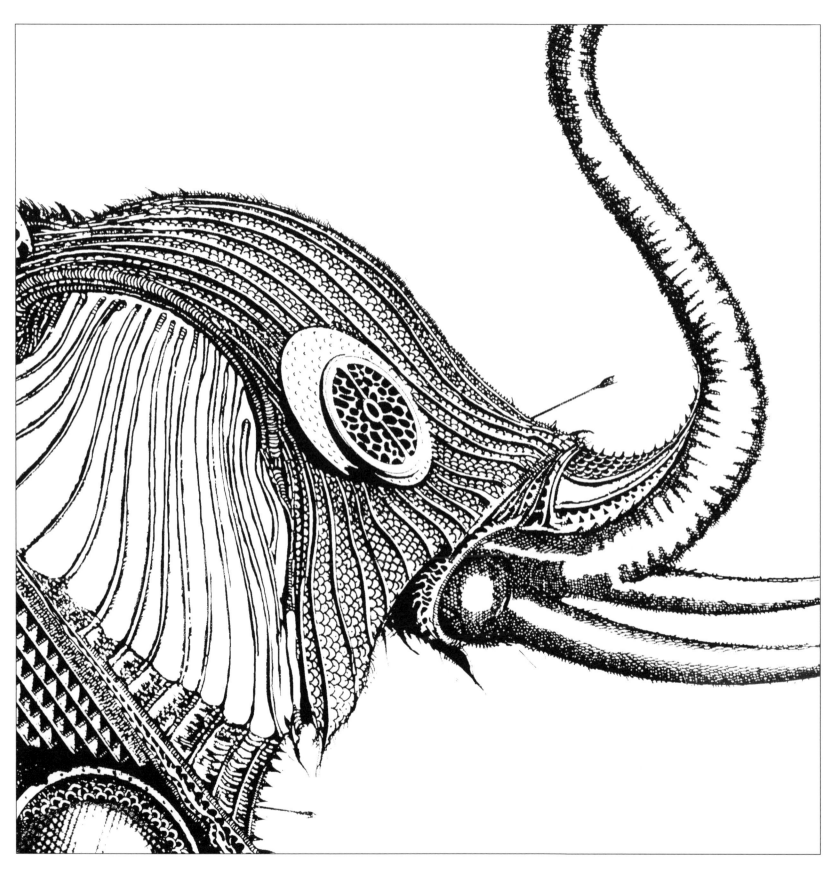

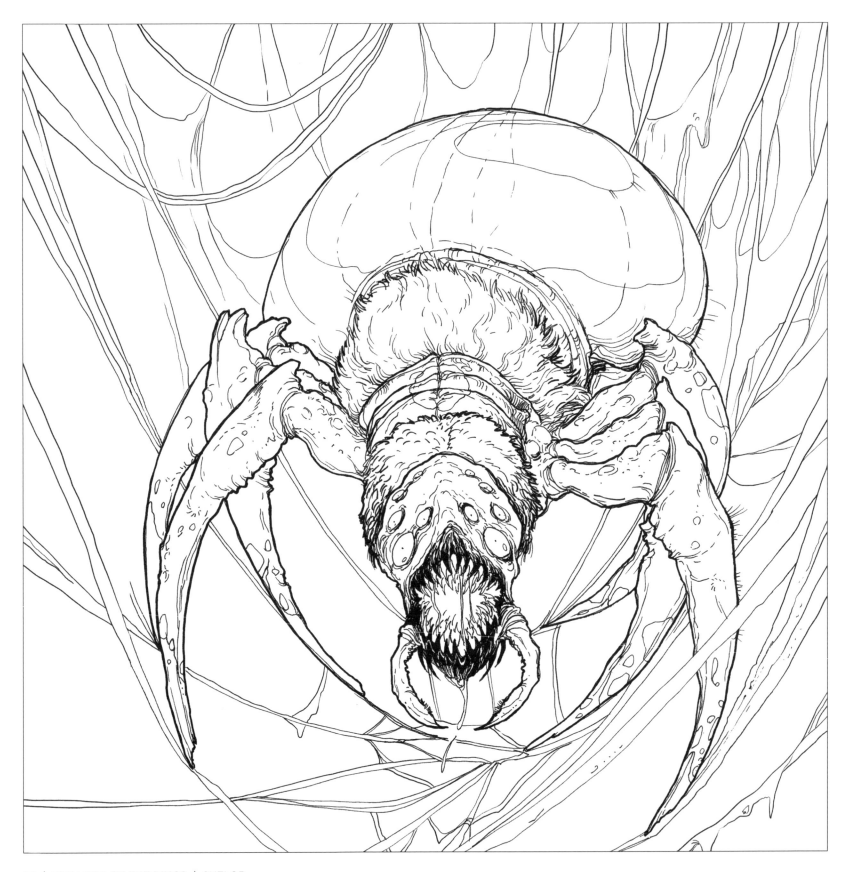

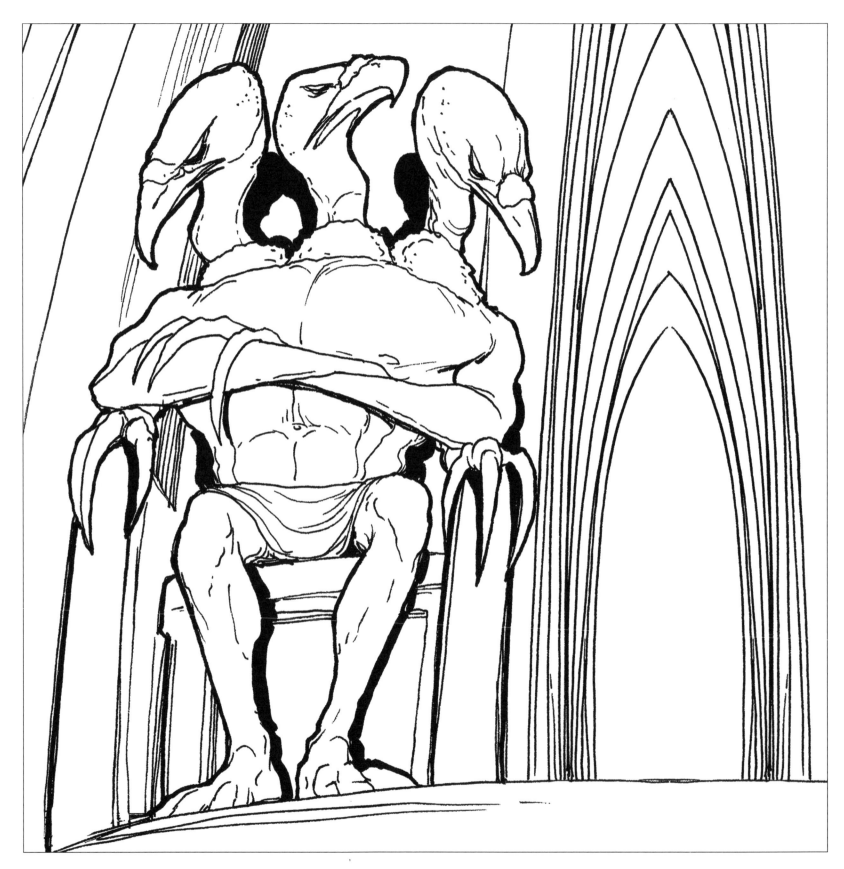